Svetlana Chmakova's
Nightschool
The Weirn Books

VOLUME TWO

Yen
Press

WHAT CAME BEFORE...

ALEX IS A YOUNG WEIRN (A PARTICULAR BREED OF WITCH) WHO HAS ALWAYS BEEN HOMESCHOOLED BY HER SISTER, SARAH, A TEACHER AT THE NIGHTSCHOOL, A PLACE OF HIGHER LEARNING FOR PARANORMAL BEINGS. DISOBEYING HER SISTER'S ORDER TO STAY HOME, ALEX VENTURES OUT TO A CEMETERY TO RESEARCH VAMPIRES, ONLY TO HAVE A VIOLENT ENCOUNTER WITH A GROUP OF HUNTERS, BEINGS WHO KEEP THE NIGHT CREATURES IN CHECK. WHILE SHE MANAGES TO ESCAPE UNHARMED, ALEX CAN'T FOR THE LIFE OF HER REMEMBER WHAT HAPPENED OR HOW SHE ARRIVED SAFELY HOME. MEANWHILE, SARAH IS LED UNSUSPECTINGLY TO A MYSTERIOUS STAIRWAY, AND UPON DESCENDING IT, THE ENTRANCE SEALS. SUDDENLY, ALL MEMORY OR EVIDENCE OF SARAH'S EXISTENCE DISAPPEARS — THAT IS, ALL MEMORY EXCEPT FOR ALEX'S! NOW ALEX IS FORCED TO VISIT THE NIGHTSCHOOL TO TRACK DOWN HER SISTER, WHILE THE HUNTERS ARE ON THE MOVE TO FIND THEIR ATTACKER...

CONTENTS

CHAPTER 7 3
CHAPTER 8 37
CHAPTER 9 65
CHAPTER 10 99
CHAPTER 11 127
CHAPTER 12 159
AFTERWORD 192

3

5

THERE'S A GLAMOUR SPELL ON THE SCHOOL, SO IT LOOKS DARK AND EMPTY.

TO GET PAST IT, YEAH, YOU NEED A NIGHTPASS...

...OR AT LEAST SOMETHING THAT PASSES FOR ONE.

OH. RIGHT.

!!

WHAT DO YOU WANT FOR ONE OF THESE?!

THE HAPPINESS OF A LADY IS ALL THE THANKS A GENTLEMAN NEEDS.

U-UM... TH-THANK YOU?

OKAY, YOU GIRLS SIT TIGHT, AND I'LL BE RIGHT BACK.

14

SARAH!!

29

41

BRUSH

FSS

SKREEEE

NOD

FOLLOW THE SAFEWAYS, DON'T STRAY.

PROTECT HER WITH YOUR LIVES.

I'LL BE BACK IN THE MORNING.

...UH.

WHAT ARE YOU DOING HERE?

DAYSCHOOL'S STARTING SOON. WHY AREN'T YOU HOME?

UM... I, UH.

...I'M NEW. I'D-I'D LIKE TO ENROLL. I WAS TOLD TO SEE THE DAY KEEPER.

ARE YOU HER?

...

TSK. LET ME GUESS, MRS. MURREY COULDN'T BE BOTHERED.

FINE. FOLLOW ME.

TAK TAK TAK

CLICK

RUSTLE

?

!!

ARGH!!
WHO'S BEEN
READING MY
BOOK?!!

OF ALL
THE...

AW, THE
COVER'S
ALL BENT.

CLEAN
CLEAN

KTK

75

. . .

THIS IS NOT A PROBLEM! I WILL EITHER FIND IT OR FIGURE IT OUT, WHICHEVER COMES FIRST.

IDEALLY BY THE TIME CLASSES START TONIGHT. OR MADAM CHEN WILL GET UNPLEASANT AGAIN.

WHEN?

TONIGHT.

....!

HOW OLD DID YOUR SEER SAY THE GIRL IS?

YOUNG. ABOUT THIRTEEN. NOT TALL, CAUCASIAN, WHITE HAIR.

HMM, A THIRTEEN-YEAR-OLD BLONDE WHO CASTS ANCIENT AND POWERFUL SPELLS...

I WONDER IF SOMEONE LIKE HER WOULD BE ATTENDING SCHOOL. WHAT ARE THE CHANCES THAT SHE'S IN MINE...?

SHE'S HOME-SCHOOLED.

AND NOT BLONDE HAIR— WHITE. AS IN GRAY.

Chapter 10

...ALSO KNOWN AS THE BENJAMIN THERON NIGHT-SCHOOL, NAMED AFTER SIR BENJAMIN THERON, A WEIRN SPELL SCIENTIST FROM BRITAIN.

THAT'S HIM UP THERE. HE'S REALLY FAMOUS BECAUSE HE REVOLUTIONIZED SPELL SCIENCE...

...BY APPLYING THE CONCEPT OF ALGORITHMS AND AXIOMS!

...

...NERD.

A-ALSO, UM! HE IS FAMOUS FOR ACCIDENTALLY SINKING AN ISLAND OFF THE SHORE OF AUSTRALIA IN ONE OF HIS EXPERIMENTS.

WOAH, COOL

OOPS

BYE!

AUSTRALIA

...WHAT?

YOU-YOU SAID THEY WERE OUT...

YEAH, SORRY, I MEANT OUT AS IN UNCONSCIOUS...

I THOUGHT YOU REMEMBERED FROM YESTERDAY.

BUT I GUESS YOU WOULDN'T, HUH.

НАДЯ, НАДЕНЬКА, ЧТО С ТОБОЙ...?

НИН?

WHY IS HER SKIN LIKE THIS?

123

129

...YOU WISHED TO BE REMINDED OF YOUR CLASS. IT IS AT MIDNIGHT.

AH, THAT'S RIGHT. THANK YOU.

IS THE HUNTER STILL AROUND?

MR. DAEMON HAS BEEN GONE FOR SOME TIME. HE LEFT A MESSAGE REQUESTING SPEED IN YOUR INVESTIGATION.

I'M SURE HE DID.

THERE IS ALSO A LEYNET MESSAGE FROM MADAM CHEN, SAYING THERE IS A PLEASANT SURPRISE WAITING FOR YOU AT THE SCHOOL.

...OH?

WELL, SOME GOOD NEWS IS DEFINITELY WELCOME TONIGHT.

OH, AND BY THE WAY, THESE ARE FOR YOU.

NEW ARRIVALS.

PLEASE TAKE CARE OF THEM.

!!

MY APOLOGIES FOR THE MESS, BUT I MUST BE GOING.

APPARENTLY, THERE IS AN ELUSIVE SILVER-HAIRED MENACE ON THE LOOSE.

AH YES. WELCOME TO YOUR 16TH ASTRAL TRAINING CLASS OF THIS SCHOOL YEAR!

WELL, PUT THOSE TEXTBOOKS AWAY, BECAUSE TODAY THERE ARE NO READING ASSIGN-MENTS!

I BET YOU ARE WONDERING WHAT SORT OF EXCITING THINGS YOU WILL BE LEARNING TODAY, RIGHT?

TODAY, YOU OFFICIALLY START TRAINING YOUR ASTRALS.

SO CALL THEM OUT, WEIRN BOYS AND GIRLS!

...!!

!!

WOO-HOO!

FINALLY

YAAA

AS WE ALL KNOW, ASTRALS ARE NOT TERRIBLY SMART, UNLIKE *REAL* DEMONS LIKE MYSELF.

THEY ARE LOYAL AS DOGS AND HAVE JUST ABOUT AS MUCH SENSE OR FINESSE... BUT!

WINGS.

I BELIEVE I JUST EARNED A PASSING GRADE IN YOUR CLASS.

WHAT NOW?

HER ASTRAL CONTROL IS UNIVERSITY LEVEL!! IF NOT HIGHER!! WHY IS SHE IN MY CLASS?!

...UNIVERSITY LEVEL? REALLY?

YES!! SHE JUST GREW FULLY-SPANNED WINGS, SUE! SHE...

HOW IMPRESSIVE! DO YOU THINK SHE'S GOOD MATERIAL FOR MR. ROI'S CLASS, THEN?

...!

...YES. OH YES, DEFINITELY.

GREAT. HE'S BEEN WANTING A NEW STUDENT TO PLAY WITH.

OOOH, HE'LL CUT YOU DOWN TO SIZE. SEE IF YOU CAN MOUTH OFF TO HIM.

161

RIGHT. WELL...I WANT TO APOLOGIZE THAT YOUR FIRST CLASS WAS SO... TURBULENT, ALEX.

I THINK YOU WILL ENJOY MR. ROI'S CLASS MORE. I VERY MUCH LOOK FORWARD TO SEEING WHAT YOU DO THERE.

...

THANK YOU, MA'AM.

"MA'AM"! YOU'RE SO POLITE.

I GIVE BACK THE RESPECT I GET, MA'AM.

...!

HOW INTERESTING.

...FOURTH...?
THERE WASN'T
A FOURTH...

...WILL SHE BE OKAY?

...

...

THE CHASE FAMILY WANTS YOU BACK. THEY SET A MEETING.

....!

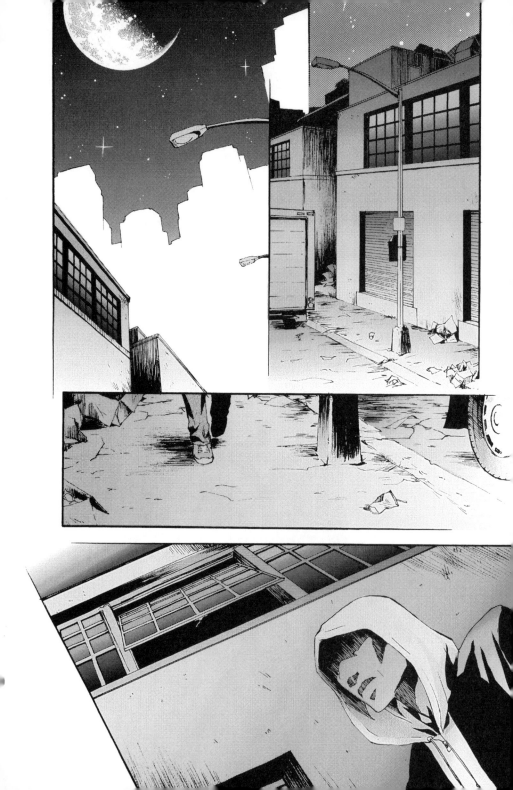

YOU-YOU SAID HE'D BRING THE SEER. WHY DOESN'T HE HAVE—

SHUT UP.

HELLO, GRAY.

HELLO, DAEMON.

WAS KINDA HOPING YOU'D SAVE ME SOME TROUBLE AND BRING THE GIRL.

183

HEH

AS FOR YOU...

...I DON'T THINK WE'LL EVEN NEED A GRAVE.

SO HOW ABOU—

TO BE CONTINUED IN NIGHTSCHOOL VOL. 3...
LOOK FOR NIGHTSCHOOL EVERY MONTH IN YEN

Now, without further ado, I will introduce the awesomeness that is the next two pages!! Many *Nightschool* readers are also talented artists, so we ran a **Fan Art Contest** to show you what they can do. It was incredibly difficult to pick only eight from all the great art we received, so we ended up with several runners-up:

Emily Adams   Julien Faille   Kaitlin Gagnon   Sarah Miller   Karen Yen

Thank you!! We hope you enjoy your prizes :).

And finally... *drumroll* The contest winners are...!

LIGHTS OUT
by *Alcina Wong*
(I-I think half the characters are here... IMPRESSIVE)

by *Morgan Zamboni*
(Yay, Mr. Roi, looking sharp in a suit!!)

by *Omnaya Omar*
(The rose in the original is a beautiful blue)

This begs the question..can he read her thoughts

Work place dating may = can of worms
Workplace Fanatasies are an entirely different matter

by *Sarah Covington*
(Wakey wakey, Sarah :D)

by **Rebecca Long**
(SO. CUTE.)

by **Merritt Zamboni**
(Alex's Amazing Astral!! Too right! <3)

by **Starlia Prichard**
(The family! Personalities
captured *perfectly*.)

by **Kaia Dumoulin**
(Originally in color, and SO beautiful...)

NIGHTSCHOOL
THE WEIRN BOOKS ②

SVETLANA CHMAKOVA

Toning Artist: Dee DuPuy

Lettering: JuYoun Lee

NIGHTSCHOOL: The Weirn Books, Vol. 2 © 2009 Svetlana Chmakova.

Yen Press
Hachette Book Group
237 Park Avenue, New York, NY 10017

Visit our Web sites at www.HachetteBookGroup.com
and www.YenPress.com.

Yen Press is an imprint of Hachette Book Group, Inc. The Yen Press name and logo are trademarks of Hachette Book Group, Inc.

First Yen Press Edition: October 2009

ISBN: 978-0-7595-2860-4

10 9 8 7 6 5 4 3 2 1

BVG

Printed in the United States of America